For my daughters, Ella and Maggie, with all of my love

Author's note:

I've always thought of "salty sleepy" as that feeling you get after a long day at the beach and right before dozing off - the best kind of happy, crispy, sandy tired. These stories were jotted down in a stack of little notebooks during my saltiest and sleepiest hours.

I've been writing poems to go along with my drawings for many years and wanted to put together a set of surf-inspired pieces. They were taken from different stages of my life... when I was learning to surf, while backpacking through Central America, during my first real job, when my (now) wife and I were dating, and since I've become a father to my beautiful daughters.

I hope you enjoy reading these stories as much as I've loved writing and drawing (then redrawing and redrawing and redrawing) them! I'm stoked to share *Salty Sleepy Surfery Rhymes* with you, and many thanks for picking up this book.

Joe Vickers

First edition

ISBN: 978-0-692-06017-9

www.JoeVickersArt.com

Salty Sleepy

SURFERY RHYMES

Surf poems and drawings
by Joe Vickers

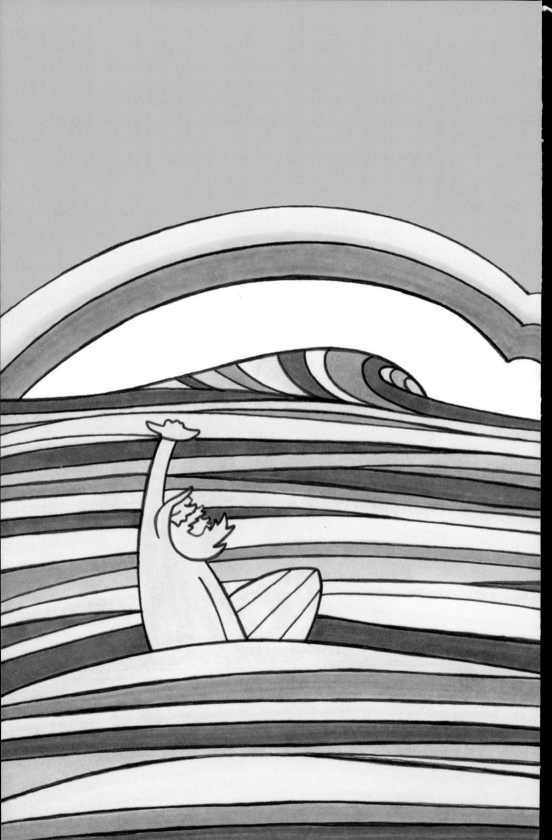

I wanted to sleep
And stay in bed,
But you made me get up
And paddle out instead.

The report said it was small,
Not much swell in the water,
But you made me go,
I wouldn't have bothered.

And the wind didn't seem
To be blowing the right way,
But you didn't care, you said,
"We're surfing today."

I said, "The water's too cold!
Let me cuddle up and snore!"
But you reminded me
That's what wetsuits are for.

And it's so early,
The sun's not even up,
But you threw me in the van,
Handed me a coffee cup.

Now the day's peaking out
Over palms on the slopes,
Turns the ocean's blues into
Green-yellow-red kaleidoscopes.

And a set just rolled through
On a long paddle out,
It's head high and glassy
And there isn't any doubt

That I'm glad I'm not in bed,
You made me stick to the plan.
I'm stoked out of my mind,
Good call, man.

I think I'll take the quad
Or maybe even the twin,
Or maybe my 9'6,
I'd like to ride it again.

I could take my single,
The tide could be swamped,
Or maybe my new handplane
And go out for a whomp.

There could be some long lines,
Man, I hope, I wish!
Perfect for my mid-length
Or my favorite fish.

I could take my groveler
'Cause I really trust her,
Change the fins around a bit
And set up like a thruster.

But what if I show up
With the wrong stick?
Then I'll sit on the beach
And cry about my pick.

It's too big of a decision,
It's just too hard to call.
The only option really is
I'll have to take them all.

She fades into the shade
As it's there she has it made,
And when it's all over
She wishes she could have stayed,

In the shade, in the shade,
She never wants to stray,
If every single hour
Of every single day,

She could stay, she could stay
Behind the blue-green shade,
There is no need to leave,
She would never go away,

Not tomorrow, not today,
She would never go away,
If she could, she would
Stay tucked into the shade.

Won't you please do play me
A song on your ukulele.
I'll set a fire for the light
If on this lovely summer night,
Please do won't you play me
A song on your ukulele.

We can sleep right here
While our wetsuits dry,
But until then
To pass the time,
Won't you please do play me
A song on your ukulele.

Your sweet sings
Over those four strings
Help me not to worry
What tomorrow brings, so
Won't you please do play me
A song on your ukulele.

"One more wave,"
I hear myself say
As I check the time and know
I should call it a day.

So I catch a little peeler
All the way to the shore,
And when my feet hit the ground
On the ocean's sandy floor, I think...

"One more wave,"
Ah, what will it hurt?
If I'm a little late
They won't miss me at my work.

So I paddle into another,
The swell is filling in steadily,
I take it to the beach
Then look back out readily, and say...

"One more wave,"
I can't give up now.
As the tide gets just right,
Leave? Ain't no way, no how!

So I find myself again
Way out the back,
The next one is so hollow
And after a solid shack, I hoot...

"One more wave!"
Then I do decree
To forget about the job,
Don't need responsibilities.

So again I'm in the lineup
Just in time for a bomb!
Stoked out of my mind
As I cruise the face so long, I scream...

"ONE MORE WAVE!!!"
So I paddle out to play.
I'll be here till nightfall,
This is where I belong today.

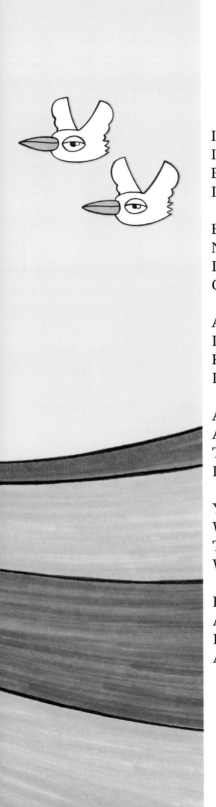

I thought that I'd drop in,
I thought that I'd score,
But what I'm thinking now
Is not what I thought before.

Because I hesitated,
Now to my dismay,
I'm sitting at the very top
On the curl of a breaking wave.

And yes I know what's next,
I've been here once or twice,
For not committing to the drop
I will have to pay the price.

At first I'll get thrown down
And land with a big splash,
Then spend some time underwater
In an all-out violent thrash.

You know it won't feel very good
When the pressure pops my ears,
The second or two that I'm held down
Will feel like several years.

But for now it's like slow motion
Atop this watery peak,
In a few minutes I'll gasp for air
And start picking sand out of my teeth.

The sun and the sand,
A board in her hand
With a smile she could never cover...
All of her days
She spends with the waves,
A mermaid's stoke is like no other...

Toeses and noses
Have always been
As thick as thieves,
The best of friends.

They love hanging out,
Going right, alright.
Don't forget a left or two
Before they tuck in for the night.

They love to work together
To cross-step down the line.
One-two-one-two-one-two,
Keeping rhythm in good time.

I would like to ask them questions,
But their answers I think I know.
I always pretend that this is how
Our conversation would go...

"Where would you like to be today,
My trusty little toeses?"
"Balanced oh so steadily,
Sliding on these noses."

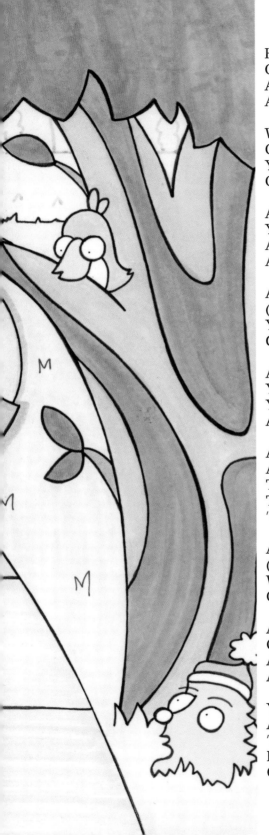

Have you ever been out
On a neighborhood walk,
And you and your doggy
Are having a little talk,

When all of a sudden,
Out of nowhere,
You see a low-hanging branch
On the sidewalk right there,

And instead of going around
Your mind starts to wander,
And you tuck into a stance
And duck right under,

And for a few seconds
(Or however long you'd please),
You're deep in a tube
Getting barreled with such ease,

And during that time
You weren't ducked under a tree,
You were oh so pitted
At Cloudbreak down in Fiji,

And the neighbors don't know,
As they puzzle
Through their window,
That to you you're stalling hard
'Cause you're shacked out in Indo,

And your doggy stares at you
(This happens time to time),
While you think you're deep
On the North Shore at Pipeline,

And as you pop out
Of a flawless barrel ride,
And you stand back up
And open your two eyes,

You look at your doggy
And continue your little talk
'Cause now you're
Feeling pretty good
On this neighborhood walk.

I heard there was a swell
So we headed to the beach,
It used to kill me when
The waves were out of reach.
But today I was content
Just to hear the ocean sing
And watch you all catch a few,
But I didn't miss a thing.

I've surfed a bit less this year,
I'm a little light on sleep.
I got in the water for one or two,
But that was sometime last week.
I know it's been a good winter
With what the swells did bring,
But I have to tell you friends
That I didn't miss a thing.

I'll be back before too long,
She's growing up each day.
We'll all head to the beach
For castles, surf, and play.
Until then when a swell comes in
I still feel a little sting,
But it doesn't matter much to me
Because I won't miss a thing.

In the land
Of the Surfosaurus,
You should be wary
'Cause he won't ignore us.

We're like chicken strips,
We taste so good.
We try to catch a few
In his neighborhood.

But just know he's watching you,
Just know that he's aware.
Just know when you hear his roar
You'll be pretty scared.

He's a monster, that's for sure,
He'd rather eat a steak.
But then he sees you sliding around
At his favorite break.

He gets so very angry
(He's a bit territorial).
He wants you gone
(Plan your memorial).

We could try to befriend him,
But let's not be heroic.
All his surfer buddies
Are from the Era Mesozoic.

OH NO, THERE HE IS!
Crashing through the trees we must
Run and hide away
From the local Surfosaurus.

Weavin' Steven
Would drop in on a bomb,
Then weavin' Steven
Would weave through the groms.

And all the groms in his line
Would laugh at Steven,
They'd get in his way on purpose
Just to see his weavin'.

And then one day
Lost his mind did Steven.
Some say it was from
All the grom weavin'.

And now the ole chap,
Well, he's a little uneven.
He wears board shorts
When it's warm or when it's freezin'.

No telling now
If he's arrivin' or he's leavin',
Or if his stories are
Lies or worth believin'.

And when he drops in
On big ole giant bombs,
He no longer dodges
The laughing little groms.

He'll head straight at them,
He's forgot about the weavin'.
Now no one ever paddles out
With crazy ole Steven.

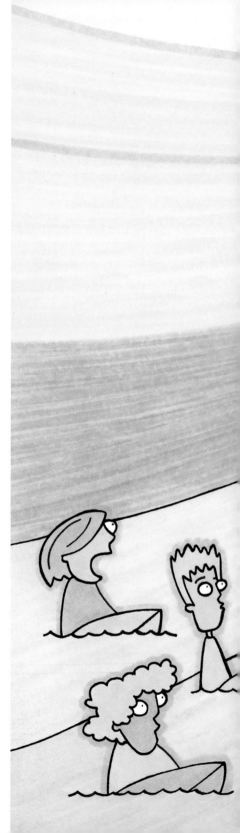

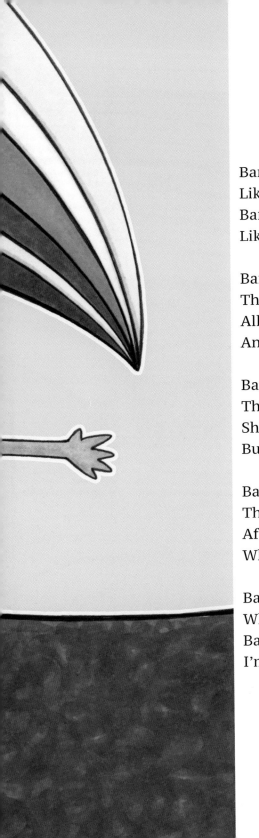

Barrels so wide
Like the length of a freight train,
Barrels so wide
Like the wings of an airplane.

Barrels so thick
That no light gets through,
All black and gray
And tinted shades of blue.

Barrels so shallow
That the reef's right there,
Sharp as a razor,
But you're not going to care.

Barrels so hollow
That there are dudes who've cried
After a twenty-second tube
When they come out the other side.

Barrels so wide
When the right swell rolls through,
Barrels like that...
I'm always looking for you.

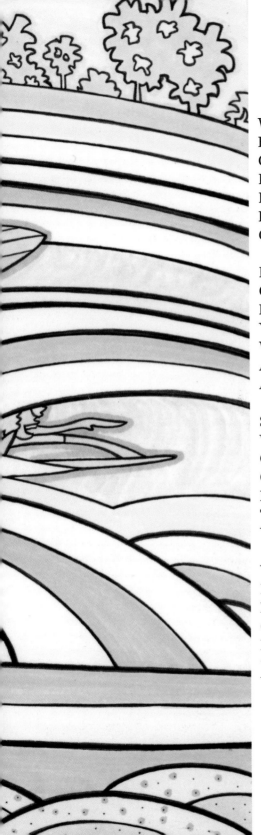

When you head to your
Beach break,
Could be good,
It could be great.
It could be tiny,
Polluted and slimy,
Or flat as a pancake.

It could be hollow
Or it could crumble,
Be so heavy
You end up humble
With a broken hand
And a head full of sand,
After a shallow tumble.

Should you get tubed
With your bros?
Or log some time
On the nose?
Better take a sec
To have a quick check,
You'll never know if you don't go.

Will you go left?
I might...
Let's split the peak,
Go right!
Doesn't matter which
'Cause next time we'll switch,
We're here as long as there's light.

Drop on in
And take a second or three
To close your eyes
And feel the energy
Of your board slip-slide
Across the face of the sea.

Connect each section
So seamlessly
With an arch in your back
And a bend in the knee.
Try to touch the sky,
Reach effortlessly.

Let your toes curl over
As you cross-step with ease,
Add a little bit of style
With movements that please,
And as the vibes radiate
Just relax, be free.

Gnarly Charlie
Is REALLY intense.
He goes so big,
It makes no sense.

If someone says, "Man,
You can't surf a wave that large,"
Gnarly paddles out
And proceeds to charge.

And he'll charge so hard
That birds can't fly,
They go into shock
And fall out of the sky.

Sharks will scream, "AAAAHHHHH"
Because his crazy, wild eyes
Scare them so much
That they run away and hide.

When pirates go to capture him
Charlie fights them all,
Then the pirates sail away
Feeling weak and small.

He can't have any friends
Or be in the social scene,
He spends his time pushing limits
To the max, past extreme.

So when you see a man who is
Oh so very gnarly,
Just know that he's the one
We all call Gnarly Charlie.

One-a turn-a Myrna
Only does one turn-a.
She'll set her line
Right on time,
It's the only one she ever learn-a.

Off the bottom to the top,
Smooth as a karate chop.
You can see her grins
As she buries her fins,
Once she starts, she won't stop.

If what she's doing you can't discern-a,
It's none of her concern-a.
When you're out the back
And hear a BOOM-SWOOSH-THWACK!
Just know, it's one-a turn-a Myrna.

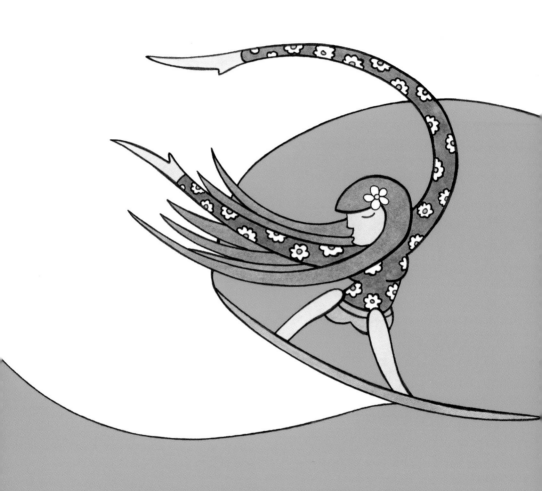

The Surf Gods and I
Don't agree
Just how much swell
There should be.
We always argue
And I say,
"LET IT RIP!
LET ME SCORE!"
They say, "Nah, less is more."
It seems as though
Today they've had their way...

I think the wind
Should always flow
From the land
Directly offshore,
Those are my favorite days.
But the Gods have it howlin'
Right into my face
Which is makin' it choppy
All over the place.
It seems as though
Today they've had their way...

And it sure would be nice
If the water was warm,
So if I forget my wetsuit
There would be no harm,
With a pair of baggies
I could get away.
But the Surf Gods make
The water so cold
That I feel like I'm
One hundred years old.
It seems as though
Today they've had their way...

You can look towards the sky
And scream bloody murder,
But you'll still be scratchin'
Through tiny mushburgers,
Keep on praying, so they say.
The Surf Gods will be
Laughing at you
Because it's up to them
When a swell comes through.
They seem as though
They always have their way...

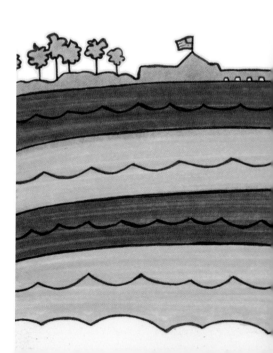

Good morning, little set,
Didn't think you'd be here yet,
Good morning to my cup of coffee too.

Good morning, morning glow,
The colors that you show,
Pretty golds on top of ocean blue.

A camera's too high tech
For my morning surf check,
Sitting in this window here will do.

I think I'll paddle out
In a minute's time about,
But would like to enjoy this for a few.

I was supposed to work
Then do some chores,
Like take out the trash
And fix my screen door,
But the surf was so good that day...

I meant to go to class
And take a midterm test,
Then get a quick trim
Because my hair was a mess,
But the surf was so glassy that day...

I wanted some new clothes
And I would've gone to shop,
But the store was only
Three-and-a-half blocks
From surf that was hollow that day...

I should've gone to the bank
To get some pocket change,
Then headed to the doctor
'Cause I was feeling pretty strange,
But the surf was firing that day...

My bike needed a new tire,
It was incredibly flat,
And I totally forgot to feed
My funky little cat
Because the surf was so big that day...

Now my house is filled with trash,
I started itching at a rash,
And it's just not cool
That I'm failing out of school,
I always have to hike
Because I never fixed my bike,
I'm completely totally broke
And my cat almost croaked,
It's probably not the best
That my hair's a bird's nest,
I'm dressed like a slob
And got fired from my job,
I'm feeling pretty blue
Because I have so much to do...
But the surf is so good today.

Instead of heading south,
Let's avoid the crowd
And go somewhere colder
Where it's quiet, not loud.

I have a little place
Where we can camp under stars,
And while we're there this place
Will go from mine to ours.

And we can build a little fire,
And we can stay as we please,
And there's a break right there
With a backdrop of tall trees.

And we can hike, we can run,
We never have to leave.
That sounds just so perfect,
Won't you go with me please?

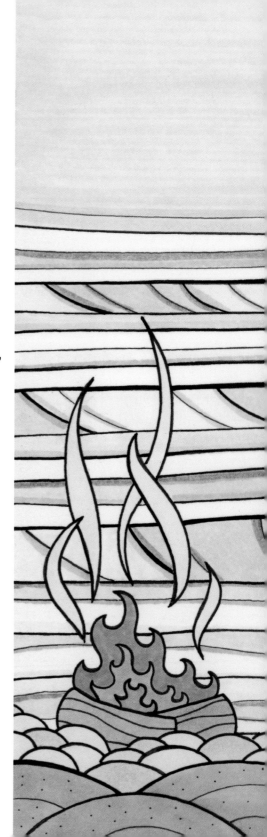

My favorite rooms
Are the ones tinted green,
But you know what I mean
If you've seen what I've seen.

When the warm Santa Anas
Make it so hollow and so clean,
You'll think you're with Bruce Brown
In an *Endless Summer* scene.

When the lip curls over
And you're slotted in between,
Then you stall till you're deep
Like a Navy submarine.

And time will be so warped,
It will feel just like a dream,
And the seconds you were covered
Were hours, so it seemed.

And during that time
It's you who feels supreme,
Like a king-shaman-wizard,
Like an enlightened being.

'Cause there's no one else on Earth
Who is seeing what you see,
And when thinking back
It will seem so serene.

But if you've seen what I've seen
Then you know what I mean,
Behind the walls of water
Tinted perfect shades of green.

You may be able
To hang five (if you try).
You may have style
Like a cool rock star guy.

You may ride the tube
Better than your bros.
You may have a nickname
Like "Baby Twinkle Toes."

You may shoot the pier
Seven days a week.
You may have a good attitude
When the outlook's bleak.

You may find a fortune
And a pot of gold.
You may still be surfing
When you're 90 years old.

You may do many things,
Some mild and some excessive,
And if you ask a mermaid,
"Aren't my moves impressive?"

She'll just smile and wave to you
While you're trying to hang ten,
'Cause you'll never
Come close to her style
When she's hanging fin.

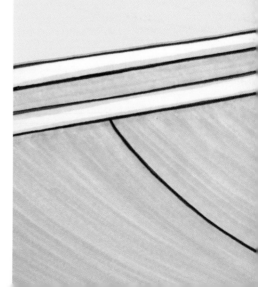

There's a ghost in the water
I wouldn't want to bother,
He's terrifying and screaming,
"BOOOOOOOOOOOOOOOOO."

Is he yelling at me?
I hope not, please.
I'd rather he shout at
YOOOOOOOUUUUUUUUU.

Oh wait, that ghost
Is just a surfer bro.
I see what he's trying to
DOOOOOOOOOOOOOOOO.

He's sick of the crowd,
He thinks they're too loud,
And he's tired of surfing with
KOOOOOOOOOOOOOOOKS.

If there was a wave that broke
For twenty-seven miles,
I'd grab my best sombrero
And cruise that wave in style.

I'd grow a big ole bushy beard,
Yeah, that's what I would do.
I'd bring my yellow single fin
And a radio for tunes.

I'd try to do some fancy tricks,
But man, I'd rather relax.
Just set my line and try to make
A few more miles of tracks.

I'd surf every inch I could
And after a quick snack,
I'd grab my board and start my walk
Twenty-seven miles back…

Sun's going down,
Gonna be dark soon.
We'll paddle out, take a breath, and
YEEEWWWWWWWW at the moon.

The water's still warm,
The time is opportune
To catch a fire, play a song, and
YEEEWWWWWWWW at the moon.

All the tourists have gone home,
Turn on the party tunes.
We can spread out, have a laugh, and
YEEEWWWWWWWW at the moon.

Some try to howl,
But us, we sing a different tune.
We stand up together and
YEEEWWWWWWWW at the moon.

They'll call us all crazy,
Think we're batty like a loon.
But we'll kick back, relax a bit, and
YEEEWWWWWWWW at the moon.

If it were up to me,
I would jump into the sea.
I'd be wild, I'd be free,
If it were up to me.

If it were up to me,
I'd paddle into wavy peaks.
I'd spend my time in the sun
For days and days and weeks.

I'd sing my own song,
"Da-da-da-da-doo-dee-dee
Da-da-da-da-doo-dee-dee,"
If it were up to me.

I'd dance all the time
With my eyes closed to the beat
Making moves up as I go
Down every single street.

Then I'd sleep all night
In between the two palm trees.
I'd do just as I please,
If it were up to me.

Then one day
As I was sitting in a tree,
I met a bird who let me know
That if I wanted to be free...

It WAS up to me!
So I jumped into the sea.
I'm wild and I'm free
Because it's up to me.

I spend my time in the sun
And paddle into wavy peaks.
I never work, I always play,
Just doing as I please.

Now I sing my little song
As I dance on down the street,
"Da-da-da-da-doo-dee-dee"
Because it's up to me.

The freaky deaky peaky
Is oh so very sneaky.
On the days
Where there's one or two waves,
A giant pops up through the haze,
It's the freaky deaky peaky.

They will catch you off guard,
When you see one, PADDLE HARD!
But it's no use,
You're going to take abuse
From the freaky deaky peaky.

Then go on, sit outside,
A long time passes by.
When you paddle in,
There it is again,
The freaky deaky peaky.

Line up with the house
Between the two tikis.
Doesn't matter much,
You're gonna get crushed
By the freaky deaky peaky.

If the groms stole Santa's sleigh,
They'd be off and on their way.
They'd load all their boards
And take off straight towards
A tropical land, far away.

On the way they'd pick up their bros,
Too many I'd have to suppose.
Blitzen would scoff
As they took off
Because of the music they chose.

They wouldn't be too specific,
Just head for the South Pacific.
Over the sea,
Make a stop in Fiji,
They heard the surf there was terrific.

They'd have the sleigh drop them out back,
And spend their time getting shacked.
They'd surf for days
Catching millions of waves
With no parents to give them flak.

Christmas would come and go,
But the groms, they wouldn't know.
If Santa doesn't bring
You a single thing,
The groms might bring it tomorrow...

I'd been waiting on these waves
For six or seven days
And man, did they provide.

There were solid head high sets,
Plenty for all to get,
But as I stood up on my first ride...

In the sky there was a blur
From a golden flying saucer,
I was beamed into space with a zap.

I always knew they'd come back to get me
Like the last time in the '80s,
But couldn't they have come when it's flat?

Salty sleepy
Salty dreamy,
From this earth
The sea will free me,
If you need to
Find or see me,
Salty sleepy
Salty dreamy...